INSIDE!

MARVEL

© 2014 MARVEL

Marvel Heroes Annual 2015 is published by Panini Publishing, a division of Panini UK Limited. Office of publication: Panini UK Ltd. Brockbourne House, 77 Mount Ephraim, Tunbridge Wells, Kent, TN4 8BS. MARVEL, SPIDER-MAN and all related characters: TM & © 2014 Marvel Entertainment, LLC and its subsidiaries. Licensed by Marvel Characters B.V. www.marvel.com. All rights reserved. No similarity between any of the names, characters, persons and/or institutions in this edition with those of any living or dead person or institution is intended, and any such similarity which may exist is purely coincidental. This publication may not be sold, except by authorised dealers, and is sold subject to the condition that it shall not be sold or distributed with any part of its cover or markings removed, nor in a mutilated condition. This publication is produced under licence from Marvel Characters, Inc. through Panini S.p.A. Printed in Italy. ISBN: 978-1-84653-195-8

D0591314

£7.99

IRON MAN'S ARMOUR

ORIGIN OF IRON MAN ARMOUR

Tony Stark created his first Iron Man armour while being held captive by the *Mandarin's* forces in Vietnam. Though crude in its appearance, this first suit was powerful enough to help him escape his captors and return to America.

Once back in the U.S., Tony decided to use his armour to help innocent people and took on the alter-ego of *Iron Man*. However, he feared that his metallic armour might scare people, so he spray painted the entire suit gold.

For his next upgrade Tony streamlined the suit's appearance. He made it much less bulky, improving the armour's movement and agility. He also changed the colour scheme to red and gold.

Though the basic shape of his suit hasn't changed, Tony Stark constantly upgrades his Iron Man armour, changing core systems and increasing the suit's power.

HEIGHT: 185 cms
WEIGHT: 111 kgs
POWER SUPPLY: 3 x SOLAR POWERED BATTERY CELLS
COMPUTING POWER: 70.5 TERAFLOP QUANTUM PROCESSORS
(CAPABLE OF SEVENTY TRILLION CALCULATIONS PER SECOND)
OPERATING TEMPERATURE:
MAX: 2000°C
MIN: -75°C

REINFORCED MOLECULAR GRID ARMOUR
The armour's outer shell is made from a light weight titanium alloy. It has been treated with a special molecular paint which makes it invisible to RADAR.

JET PACK
Maximum flight speed of 960 mph.

SUPER HERO STYLE!

Check out some of the special Iron Man suits Tony Stark has created!

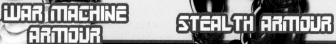

WAR MACHINE ARMOUR   **STEALTH ARMOUR**   **AQUATIC ARMOUR**   **ARCTIC ARMOUR**

4

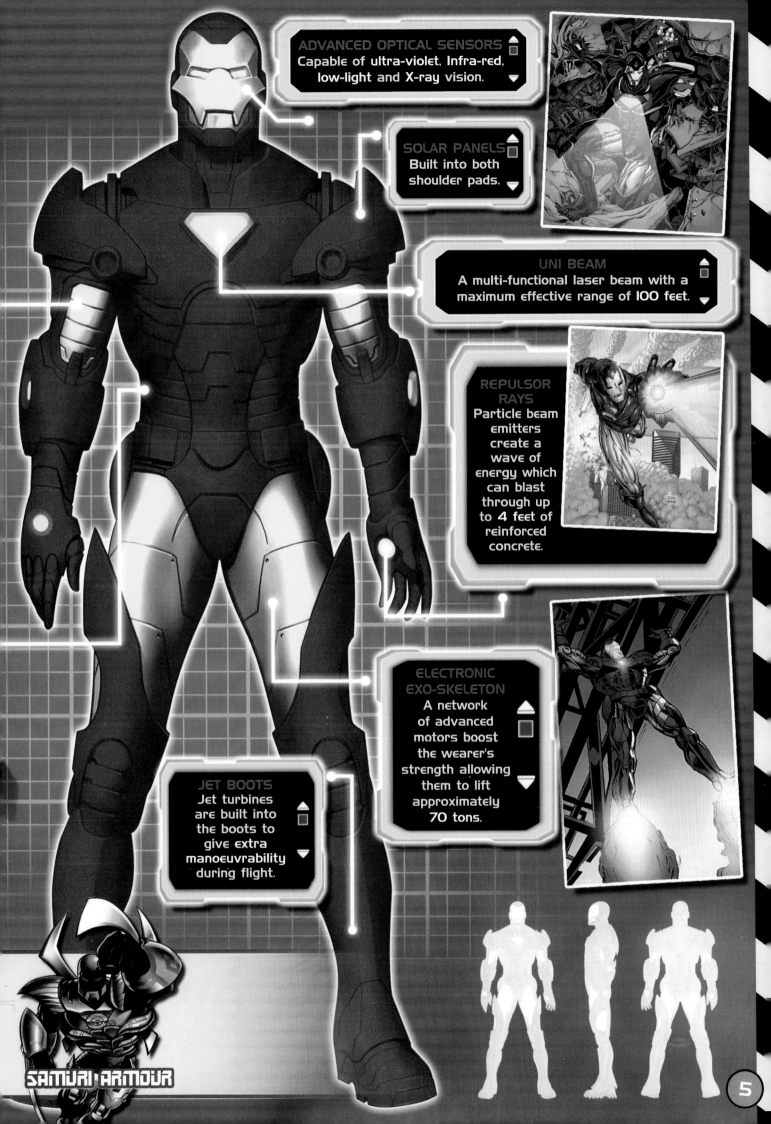

ADVANCED OPTICAL SENSORS
Capable of ultra-violet, Infra-red, low-light and X-ray vision.

SOLAR PANELS
Built into both shoulder pads.

UNI BEAM
A multi-functional laser beam with a maximum effective range of 100 feet.

REPULSOR RAYS
Particle beam emitters create a wave of energy which can blast through up to 4 feet of reinforced concrete.

ELECTRONIC EXO-SKELETON
A network of advanced motors boost the wearer's strength allowing them to lift approximately 70 tons.

JET BOOTS
Jet turbines are built into the boots to give extra manoeuvrability during flight.

SAMURI ARMOUR

5

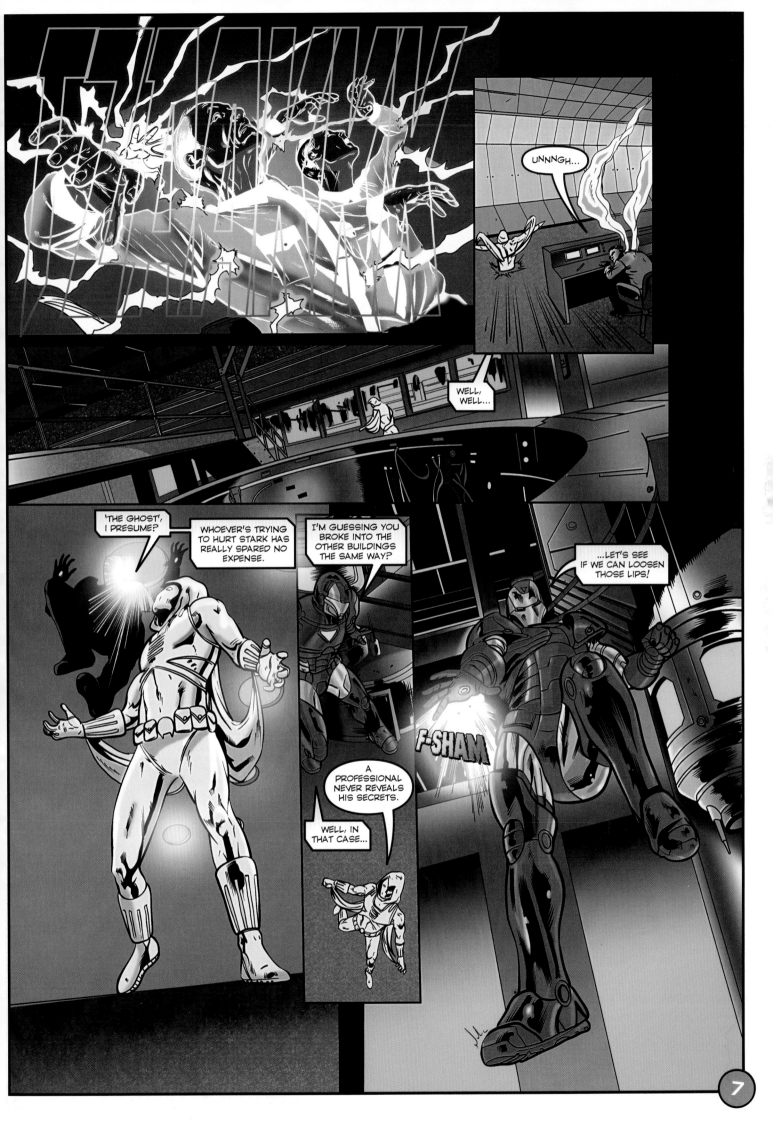

IRON MAN

ARMOUR UP!

Listen up, gang. Tony Stark was just in the middle of designing some new armour, but was called away on an urgent mission as Iron Man. Help him finish these blueprints by sketching a butt-kicking new battle-suit!

IRON MAN

IRON MAN ARMOR: ACTIVATE!

HERO FACTS:

To protect his secret identity, Tony Stark has told the world that Iron Man is actually his personal bodyguard.

ORIGINAL MK#1 ARMOUR

Stark Industries is under attack by the evil robot **Ultron!** Captain America and Iron Man are on the scene ready to stop the *metallic menace*, so help them out by solving these puzzles!

ULTRON!

A cruel and cunning cyborg with one mission – to wipe out organic life and create a planet *ruled* by robots!

CLONE ZONE!

MISSION I

Ultron has created 3 evil robotic copies of famous heroes! Help Iron Man take them down by working out which characters they are based on!

A.

B.

C.

ARMS RACE!

MISSION 2

Captain America has discovered that Ultron is after the advanced weapons technology hidden in the factory's vaults. Can you work out which route Cap needs to take to get there whilst avoiding Ultron's guards?

WEAPONS STORAGE NO ENTRY!

START:

FINISH:

ROBOT WARS!

CAPTAIN AMERICA · THE INVINCIBLE IRON MAN

MISSION 3

Iron Man's lasers can't break through Ultron's adamantium skin! His only chance is to hack into the metal monster's systems and upload a computer virus. Help Iron Man break through Ultron's security systems by solving this code!

CODE CRACKER!

ENCRYPTED MESSAGE:

CODE:

ギ=A ゴ=B ·ノ=C ·ll=D
テ=E ハ=F ギ=G ク=H
ハ=I レ=J ブ=K ペ=L
ボ=M ビ=N ダ=O ズ=P
ド=Q ガ=R ビ=S デ=T
ザ=U ヲ=V ''=W l..=X
ニ=Y 土=Z

PASSWORD:

EXPERT AIM!

MISSION 4

Iron Man's plan worked and Ultron is off-line. A few of his droids are still causing trouble though. Cap can take them down by hurling his shield, but it's up to you to help him hit them.

Study this picture for 20 seconds, then shut your eyes. Using a pen, try to draw a dot on each robot's target without peaking. Good luck!

15

Brilliant scientist Dr Henry 'Hank' Pym is the inventor of an amazing size-changing chemical known as **Pym Particles**. This incredible compound can drastically alter the size of any object, causing it to shrink or grow.

TINY TERRORS!

The first time Hank successfully shrank his own body he was attacked by **ants** from a nearby nest. Pym managed to escape and restored himself to normal size. However, his close shave with the ants had given him an idea...

HALF-INCH HERO!

After extensive research, Hank built a **cybernetic helmet** that allowed him to talk to and control ants. With this size-altering powers and a potentially unstoppable army of ant-helpers at his disposal, he became the Astonishing Ant-Man!

NAME: Henry "Hank" Pym
HEIGHT: 182 cms
WEIGHT: 86 kgs
EQUIPMENT:
Pym Particles and a cybernetic helmet.
POWERS | ABILITES:
Size-alteration, communication with ants and enhanced strength when shrunk. He is also highly intelligent and an expert at cybernetics.

THE ASTONISH ANT-MA

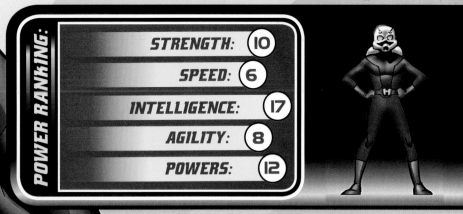

POWER RANKING:	STRENGTH:	10
	SPEED:	6
	INTELLIGENCE:	17
	AGILITY:	8
	POWERS:	12

ANT-MAN FACT:

When Ant-Man shrinks in size, he still retains his normal level of strength making him super strong!

ANT ATTACK!

Ant-Man has invented his own trademark form of *Ant-judo* that uses this super strength to its full advantage.

ANT-MAN FACT:

Hank Pym was a founding member of the Avengers, along with Iron Man, Thor, Hulk and the Wasp.

ANT-MAN FACT:

He has also used the size-altering power of the Pym Particles to become a giant-sized Super Hero called Goliath. ▶

NG N!

MARVEL ▶▶▶
MASTERPIECE!

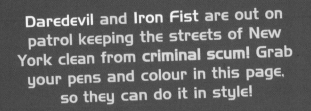

Daredevil and Iron Fist are out on patrol keeping the streets of New York clean from criminal scum! Grab your pens and colour in this page, so they can do it in style!

The Wrecking Crew are on the rampage, so help the Avengers defeat them by completing these missions!

THE WRECKING CREW

Super-powered demolition experts who use their destructive skills to cause chaos!

BULLDOZER

▲ Specialises in ramming his victims with his armoured helmet!

PILEDRIVER

▲ His huge fists can take down even the toughest heroes!

THUNDERBALL

▲ He's the brains of the organisation and carries a huge ball and chain!

WRECKER

▲ The team's leader. His crowbar has magical properties and is indestructible!

1 MULTIPLE MENACE!

MISSION 1

Thunderball's latest blow has caused Iron Man's sensors to malfunction! Can you help him by spotting which of the 5 guys on his display is an *exact match* to the original? ▶▶▶

A. B. C. D. E.

2 ARROW ATTACK!

MISSION 2

Hawkeye has let rip with a *flurry of arrows* to take down Piledriver. Follow the paths to find out which one will hit him!

A.
B.
C.
D.

WRECK AND ROLL!

AVENGERS ASSEMBLE!

VISION

IRON MAN

HAWKEYE

CAPTAIN AMERICA

SCARLET WITCH

THOR

3 PATH OF VICTORY!

MISSION 3

Captain America, Scarlet Witch, Thor and Vision have nearly caught up with Wrecker and Bulldozer. Can you work out which Avenger will reach them first?

START

START

START

START

FINISH

AVENGERS ASSEMBLE!

New York is under attack from a monster-sized menace and it's up to the Avengers to save the city. Before the adventure begins, check out which six team members have been hand-picked for this highly dangerous mission!

GIANT MAN

Real Name: Dr Hank Pym

- Scientific genius.
- Able to grow up to 60 feet tall or shrink to a microscopic size.
- Accidentally invented the deranged human-hating robot Ultron. (But try not to remind him about that one...)

IRON MAN

Real Name: Tony stark

- Billionaire playboy.
- Genius weapons inventor and pilot of hi-tech armoured battle suits.
- Excellent taste in clothes.

THOR

Real Name: Dr Donald Blake / Thor Odinson

- God of Thunder. 'Nuff said!

WASP

Real Name: Janet Von Dyne

- Shrinking powers.
- Flight.
- Bio-electrical blasts.
- Girlfriend of Hank Pym. (You know, the guy who invented the human-hating robot Ultron...)

MS. MARVEL

Real Name: Carol Danvers

- Super strength.
- Flight.
- Control of cosmic energy.
- Living embodiment of Girl Power!

HAWKEYE

Real Name: Clint Barton

- Olympic-level athlete.
- Expert marksman.
- Quiver full of trick arrows.
- Loves the sound of his own voice.

COULD YOU BE AN AVENGER?

You've seen the world's greatest Super Hero team in action, now discover whether you've got what it takes to join the hallowed ranks of the Avengers!

Answer these questions and then check at the end to see how well you did!

1 GENERAL KNOWLEDGE

Who were the founding members of the Avengers?

A Thor, Iron Man, Hulk, Ant-Man and the Wasp

B Spider-Man, Wolverine, Daredevil, the Thing and Storm

C Dr Doom, the Kingpin, the Red Skull, Rhino and Galactus

What is the Avengers transport jet better known as?

A The Quinjet

B The Blackbird

C The Pogoplane

2 OBSERVATION

Which of the people below is a notorious Super Villain?

A Dr Doom

B The Punisher

C Jarvis

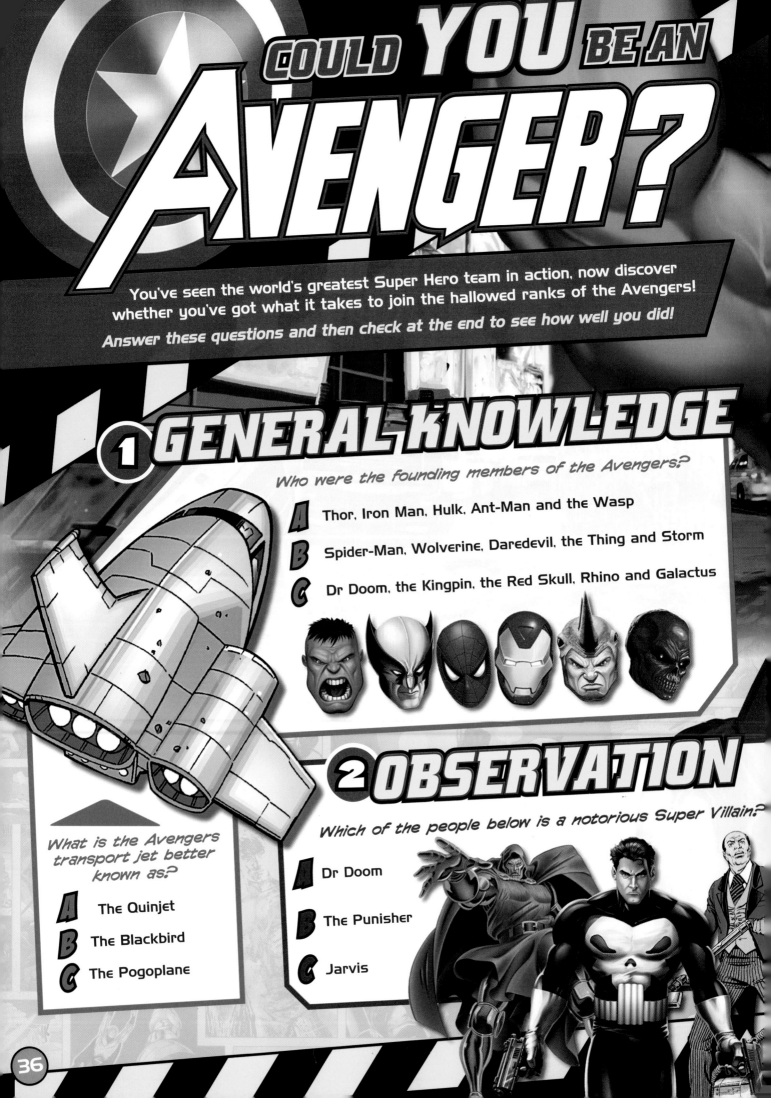

The Hulk is on the rampage and you're the only hero around. Do you...

A Lure the Hulk into an unpopulated area and then try to restrain him.

B Attack the Hulk immediately, and take him down as fast as you can.

C Try to calm him down with the offer of a cup of tea and a nice slice of fruitcake.

After foiling a robbery you spot a bag of money that has been left behind. There's no one around so do you...

A Hand the money in to the authorities.

B Use the money to buy a jetpack so you can reach the scene of a crime in double speed.

C Keep the money and spend it on a party for all your Super Hero teammates.

Which member of the Avengers does this weapon belong to?

A Thor

B Iron Man

C Vision

HOW DID YOU DO?

MOSTLY As – Congratulations! You've got just what it takes – consider yourself an honorary member of the Avengers!

Mostly Bs – Good try, but you're still not ready to join the team.

Mostly Cs – Um... Did you pick up the wrong book by accident? Maybe Knitwear Enthuasiast is more your style.

CLOSE ENCOUNTERS!

Take a trip into space and you'll discover that the Marvel Universe is teeming with extra terrestrial creatures! From the shape-shifting Skrulls to the insect-like Brood, there's more life out there amongst the stars than you'll find in Wolverine's socks!

Test your alien knowledge by seeing if you can spot the names of all these races in the giant word grid below!

- SPACE PHANTOMS
- BEYONDERS
- DIRE WRAITHS
- BROOD
- RIGELLIANS
- KREE
- BADOON
- SHI'AR
- CELESTIALS
- PHALANX
- WATCHERS
- SYMBIOTES
- TECHNARCHY
- SKRULL

"...BECAUSE WE'RE GOING TO HAVE TO DO THIS THE *HARD* WAY."

HULK, PLEASE, THIS ISN'T WHAT IT SEEMS.

NOT BETTY. *FAKE!* HULK REMEMBER NOW.

IT'S NO GOOD, MAJOR, HE'S GOING GREEN.

BLAST, I *KNEW* THIS WOULD HAPPEN. JUST TRY AND GET IT TO STALL HIM...

YES, BUT I NEED YOU TO TRUST ME. YOU DON'T KNOW WHAT'S AT *STAKE* HERE...

HULK DON'T CARE. ONLY *ENEMIES* TRICK HULK--

BRAVO BASE TO ALL UNITS. *PROCEED WITH CAUTION,* OVER.

ROGER THAT, BRAVO BASE.

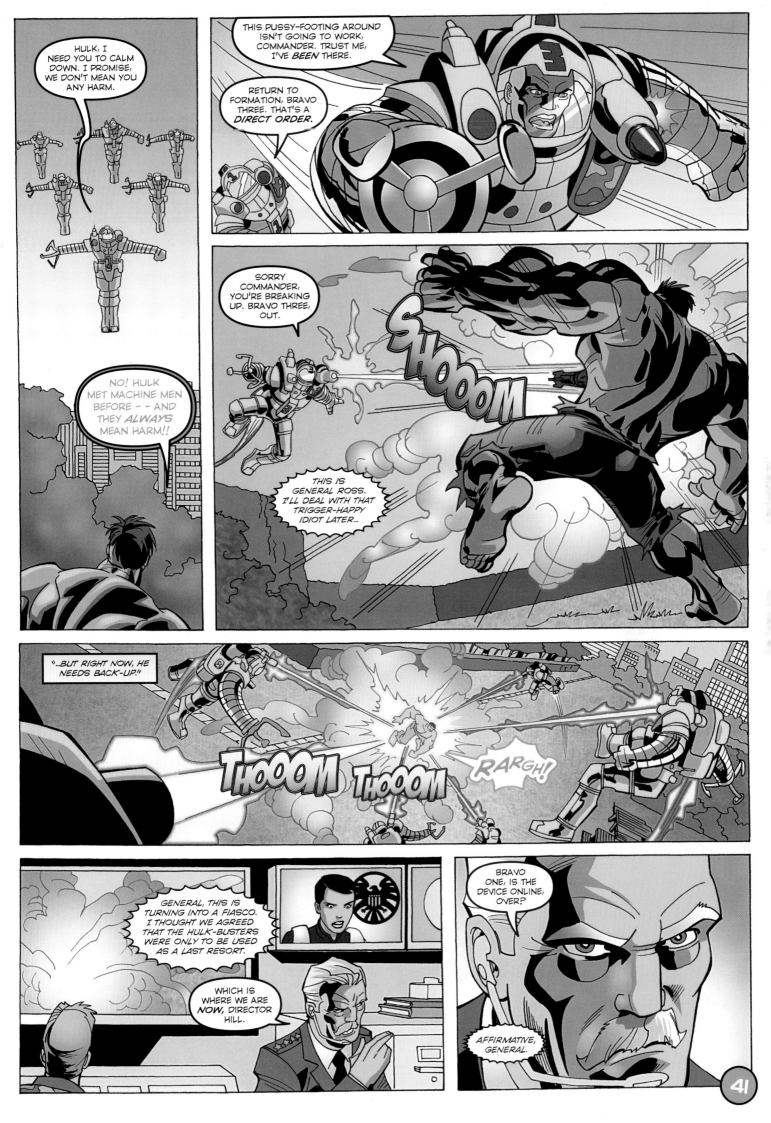

...BUT WHATEVER IT IS, IT ISN'T WORKING.

HUH? WAIT, THE HULK... HE'S GONE...

...I'M IN CONTROL NOW!

THUNDERBOLT ROSS. I MIGHT HAVE KNOWN YOU'D BE INVOLVED.

BRUCE, I APOLOGISE FOR OUR METHODS. BUT THIS REALLY IS AN EMERGENCY.

AND SO YOU KNOW, THE DEVICE IS AN EXPERIMENTAL PROTOTYPE.

BECAUSE RIGHT NOW, WE NEED YOU IN CONTROL OF THAT MONSTER'S BODY.

BUT WHY? I MEAN IT, I WANT SOME ANSWERS... AND DON'T EVEN THINK ABOUT LYING TO ME.

WE WON'T, BRUCE. NOT WITH SO MUCH AT STAKE.

S.H.I.E.L.D. HELICARRIER. 16:40 HOURS.

OKAY, BRUCE, HERE IT IS.

SEVERAL YEARS AGO, AN ALIEN RACE CALLED THE D'BARI WERE WIPED OUT IN A CATASTROPHE...

"...BUT WE NOW KNOW A ROGUE FACTION SURVIVED - - BECAUSE FORTY-EIGHT HOURS AGO, THEIR CITY-SIZED SPACE CRAFT APPEARED IN NEAR-EARTH ORBIT!"

THEIR COMMANDER THEN MADE A BROADCAST, SAYING THAT HIS FORCES ARE POISED TO ATTACK, WITH A VIEW TO COLONISING THE PLANET.

HOWEVER, HE WANTS THE GLOBAL INFRASTRUCTURE INTACT, WHICH MEANS AVOIDING COLLATERAL DAMAGE...

44

...SO HE ISSUED A CHALLENGE. OUR MIGHTIEST HUMAN CHAMPION -- WHICH PRECLUDES THOR AND OTHER GODS -- IS TO FIGHT *THEIR* CHAMPION IN MORTAL COMBAT.

YES, IT'S SOME SORT OF WARRIOR-HONOUR THING. AND IF YOU WIN, HE'S PROMISED TO FIND ANOTHER SUITABLE TARGET.

BUT FAIL, AND THE WORLD IS THEIRS. YOU SEE...

"...THEY'VE ALREADY DEMONSTRATED THEIR TECH ON THE LUNAR SURFACE. SOME SORT OF ANTI-MATTER WEAPON THAT CREATED A SCAR VISIBLE FROM EARTH ...

"...AND BELIEVE YOU ME, WE WOULDN'T LAST FIVE MINUTES AGAINST *THAT* SORT OF FIREPOWER."

OF COURSE, THE AVENGERS, FANTASTIC FOUR AND OTHER GROUPS ARE ON STANDBY IF YOU FAIL, BUT WE DOUBT THEY'D SURVIVE FOR LONG.

SO THAT'S WHY WE, OR SHOULD I SAY *S.H.I.E.L.D.,* NEED YOU. PERSONALLY, I'VE GOT MY DOUBTS, CONSIDERING YOUR PAST RECORD.

SEEMS I DON'T HAVE A CHOICE THEN. BUT YOU *PEOPLE*...

I KNOW, BRUCE. BUT YOU'RE FINALLY IN CONTROL OF THE HULK, SURELY THAT'S A POSITIVE?

ADMIRAL J'ANAK, THIS IS ROSS. TWO WORDS -- IT'S ON.

EXCELLENT GENERAL. BUT BE SWIFT...

"...OUR CHAMPION IS HARDLY KNOWN FOR HIS PATIENCE."

ESPECIALLY WHEN THERE'S A FEE AT STAKE. YES?

CONTINUED ON PAGE 50!

45

ULTIMATE HULK-OUTS!

HULK VS. WOLVERINE

Did you know that **Wolverine's** first ever comic book appearance was in a scrap with the **Incredible Hulk?** Talk about diving in at the deep end! Even with his adamantium claws and healing factor, Wolvie was totally outclassed and ended up taking a hulk-sized beating!

HULK VS. ABOMINATION

KGB Agent **Emil Blonsky** exposed himself to massive bouts of gamma radiation on purpose in order to turn himself into the **Abomination**. He has all of the Hulk's powers, plus he's **twice as strong**. So strong in fact, that he actually managed to defeat the **Hulk** the first time they fought! Unfortunately for Abomination, in every rematch they've had since, the Hulk has wiped the floor with him!

Listen up, Hulk-heads! You've seen the green-skinned goliath in action, now read on to discover five more of the Hulk's top battles!

HULK VS. HULK

Maestro is a possible future version of the Hulk who was driven mad by intense radiation poisoning. He ruled over the Earth until the present day Hulk was sent into the future to stop him. Unable to beat him physically, the Hulk sent Maestro back in time, appearing right next to the gamma bomb which gave the Hulk his powers, seconds before it exploded. The resulting gamma blast destroyed Maestro instantly!

HULK VS. THE RED KING

Whilst exiled on the alien planet Sakaar, the Hulk was forced to become a gladiator, fighting mighty beasts in an arena for the enjoyment of the planet's tyrant the Red King. The Hulk, along with a band of fellow gladiators, managed to gain their freedom and fought the corrupt ruler. Hulk eventually destroyed the Red King in a one-on-one battle and was crowned the Planet Sakaar's new leader.

HULK VS. THE ENTIRE WORLD!!!

After returning to Earth following his time on Sakaar, the Hulk was madder than ever! With his band of former gladiators, he waged a war against the world's Heroes who he blamed for his exile. Though the Hulk was eventually defeated, the battle was so intense that the shockwaves nearly split the Earth's crust in two!

ANDROID ASSASSIN!

Famed (and feared) throughout the galaxy, Death's Head is a no-nonsense bounty hunter with a cool business-like mind. Only interested in the money, Death's Head guarantees to always get the job done no matter what obstacles stand in his way.

EXTRAORDINARY ENCOUNTERS!

This cold, logical determination to complete his mission has taken Death's Head to some unbelievable places. He's journeyed to a dimension inhabited by giant robots, encountered a meddling time-traveller and even visited Earth in the year 8162!

TRICKED, YES? TRICKED BY A FEEBLE TIME TRAVELLER AND *DUMPED HERE!* ✱

BUT AS I ALWAYS SAY IN THESE SITUATIONS, DON'T GET MAD...

...KILL SOMETHING, YES?

NAME: DEATH'S HEAD
HEIGHT: 215cm
WEIGHT: 277kg
ABILITIES:
First-rate hunting and tracking skills, extensive knowledge of hand-to-hand combat and a crack shot with rifles and pistols.

SOME PEOPLE CALL ME A *BOUNTY HUNTER*, BUT NEVER *TWICE*, YES?

If there's one thing that really grinds Death's Heads gears, it's being called a Bounty Hunter. He prefers to be known as a Freelance Peacekeeping Agent!

DEATH'S HEAD

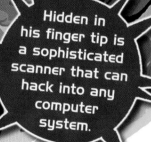

Hidden in his finger tip is a sophisticated scanner that can hack into any computer system.

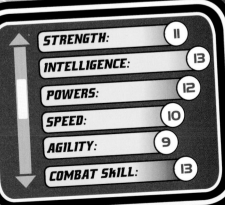

He has jets in his boots that allow him to fly at supersonic speeds.

ARMED AND DANGEROUS!

Death's Head can remove one of his hands and replace it with different weapons including a powerful blaster, a missile launcher and a huge selection of razor-sharp blades and axes.

STRENGTH:	11
INTELLIGENCE:	13
POWERS:	12
SPEED:	10
AGILITY:	9
COMBAT SKILL:	13

THE BLUE AREA OF EARTH'S MOON-- A VAST, CRUMBLING CITY CREATED MILLENNIA AGO BY THE KREE.

STILL POSSESSING A BREATHABLE ATMOSPHERE, IT IS THE PERFECT ARENA TO DECIDE THE EARTH'S FATE...

"I DON'T THINK I NEED TO REMIND YOU, BANNER...

YOU DON'T. I'M PERFECTLY ₹UNGH₹ AWARE WHAT'S AT STAKE HERE.

... BUT THE FUTURE OF MANKIND IS RESTING SQUARELY ON THOSE OVER-DEVELOPED DELTOIDS OF YOURS.

YOU'VE ₹NGH₹ GONE TO GREAT LENGTHS TO ENSURE THAT BRUCE BANNER CALLS THE SHOTS AND NOT ₹UNGH₹ THE HULK!

THE BRUTE AND THE BOUNTY HUNTER!

SCRIPT: SIMON FURMAN   PENCILS AND INKS: SIMON WILLIAMS   COLOURS: JASON CARDY & KAT NICHOLSON   LETTERS: TIM WARRAN-SMITH   STRIP EDITOR: ED HAMMOND

S.H.I.E.L.D. LUNAR COMMAND MODULE.

IT'S AS YOU FEARED, GENERAL ROSS. BANNER'S VITAL STATS ARE STARTING TO PEAK...

HEART RATE, BRAINWAVE ACTIVITY... THE NEURAL REGULATOR IS BURNING ITSELF OUT TRYING TO COMPENSATE.

"WE DON'T HAVE MUCH TIME BEFORE HE LOSES IT COMPLETELY!"

S.H.I.E.L.D. HELICARRIER, EARTH.

BLAST IT! -- I KNEW THEIR GIZMO WOULDN'T KEEP THAT MONSTER AT BAY FOR LONG --

WHAT'S THE DELAY?!

50

SO. WE REWARD THE HULK FOR SAVING THE *ENTIRE* WORLD BY ROUNDLY KICKING HIM WHILE HE'S DOWN?

SON...

"... WE'LL MAKE A FOUR-STAR GENERAL OUT OF YOU YET!"

FSSST

MEANWHILE...

I HEAR YOUR OBJECTIONS, G'ASPX, BUT THE MATTER IS *CLOSED.* WE ARE COMMITTED!

FAH! IT IS A POOR STATE OF AFFAIRS INDEED WHEN THE D'BARI TURN TO A *BOUNTY HUNTER* TO FIGHT THEIR BATTLES!

MY OWN LIFEMATE, K'HARI, WAS TAKEN FROM ME BY ONE OF THEIR KIND*! YOU ALL KNOW THIS... AND DESPITE MY VETO YOU STILL PROCEED.

*NAMELY TYRUS KRILL

CONSENSUS WAS REACHED. OUR OWN RESOURCES ARE *ACUTELY LIMITED.* WE HAD NO *CHOICE* BUT TO USE AN EXTERNAL AGENT.

EVEN OUR SHOW OF FORCE WAS A *BLUFF.* USING THE ANTI-MATTER CANNON LEFT US WITH *TOO LITTLE* ENERGY TO FULLY POWER OUR *SHIELDS.*

VERY WELL. BUT IN K'HARI'S NAME I SWEAR...

... DEATH'S HEAD WILL NOT LIVE TO SPEND HIS BLOOD MONEY!

CREATE YOUR OWN...

Check it out, True Believers. Think you've got what it takes to design a Super Hero worthy of standing shoulder to shoulder with the likes of Spidey and Iron Man? Then grab your pens and read on...

1 POWER!

First off, your hero is going to need some pretty cool powers if he's going to be fighting Super Villains. They can be as weird and whacky as you like – remember, anything is possible in the mighty world of Marvel!

HERO TIP!

Stuck for a Super Power idea? Just look at the world around you! Spidey co-creator Stan Lee was inspired to give the Web-Head wall-crawling abilities after watching a fly walk up his office wall!

2 COSTUME!

Next up, think about what your hero is going to wear. You need something striking that will make evildoers think twice about messing with your hero, but not so scary that members of the public won't trust them.

Here's a few good and bad costume ideas to help you out...

👍 HERO STYLE!

Accessory belt
Amour plating
Cape
Facemask

ZERO STYLE! 👎

Flip-flops
Handbag
Mittens
Clown nose

3 WEAPONS!

Whether it's Captain America's shield, the Silver Surfer's surfboard or Spidey's web-slingers, every hero needs a cool accessory – so add one to your hero as a final touch!

SUPER HERO

HERO NAME: ▶▶▶

SECRET IDENTITY:

SUPER POWERS & ABILITIES:

All heroes need a cool logo – design one for your costumed crusader in this box!

ANSWERS

14 ROBOT WARS!

CLONE ZONE!

Spider-Man

Mr Fantastic

Wolverine

ARMS RACE!

START:

FINISH:

CODE CRACKER!
ROBOTS RULE

26 WRECK AND ROLL!

Multiple Menace
D is the Match.

Arrow Attack
Arrow B

Path of Victory
Thor

38 CLOSE ENCOUNTERS!